MARVEL

THE MIGHTY AVENGERS ™

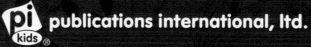

pi kids® publications international, ltd.

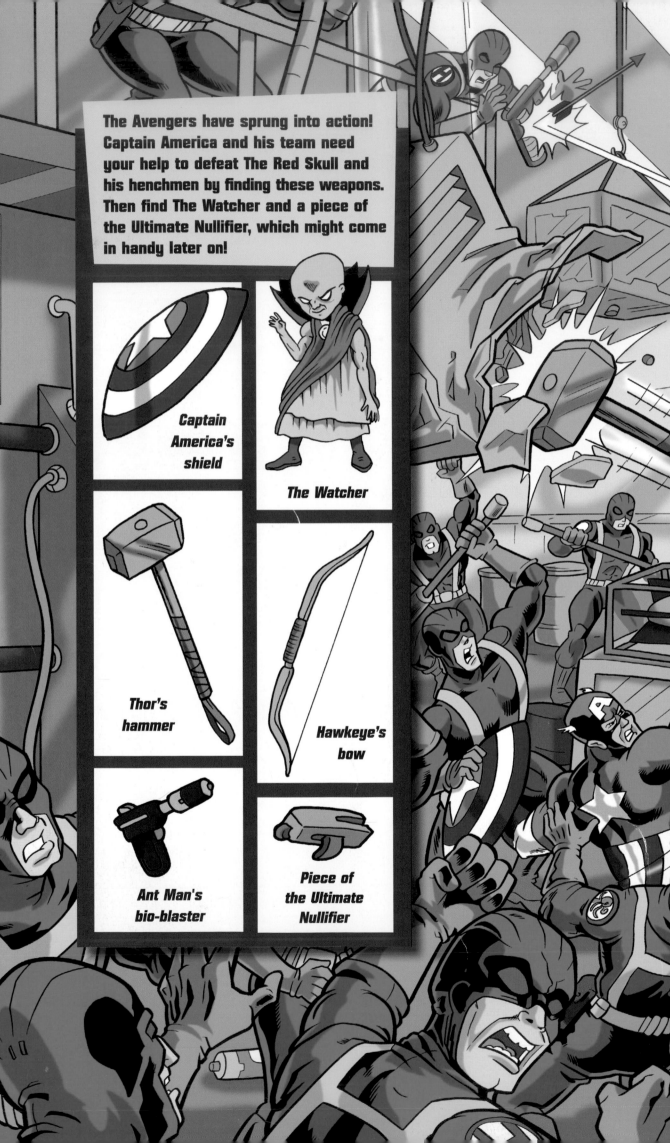

The Avengers have sprung into action! Captain America and his team need your help to defeat The Red Skull and his henchmen by finding these weapons. Then find The Watcher and a piece of the Ultimate Nullifier, which might come in handy later on!

Captain America's shield

The Watcher

Thor's hammer

Hawkeye's bow

Ant Man's bio-blaster

Piece of the Ultimate Nullifier

Thor's brother Loki has brought big trouble to the big city. Aid our favorite hammer-wielding hero and The Avengers and find these city workers who need help, along with The Watcher and another piece of the Ultimate Nullifier.

Firefighter

Police officer

Street vendor

The Watcher

Piece of the Ultimate Nullifier

Letter carrier

This construction worker

Magneto and other enemies of our heroes have decided to attack the X-Men's academy. Only Iron Man and The Avengers can help stop them. Look and find these mutant parts and pieces that will end the villains' awful onslaught.

Professor X's wheelchair

Angel's wings

The Watcher

Piece of the Ultimate Nullifier

Chunk of Iceman's ice

Wolverine's claws

Cyclops's visor

Evil never lets up. The Avengers find themselves in a graveyard full of spooks and ghouls. Help our heroes spot these creepy creatures, then look for The Watcher and another piece of the Ultimate Nullifier.

This ghost

This zombie

The Watcher

This goblin

A vampire

Piece of the Ultimate Nullifier

It's a sunny summer day at the beach. People were enjoying the weather and the water, but now The Leader and The Abomination have begun to wreck this beautiful day. Help Hulk, Thor, and the rest of The Avengers find these folks in need of a hand, as well as a couple other things.

Strong man

Surfer

This kid

This woman

Lifeguard

Piece of the Ultimate Nullifier

The Watcher

Many thieves and thugs have brought their criminal ways to this warehouse at the wharf. Only Iron Man, Hulk, and The Avengers can stop them. Sift through the action and spot these villains giving our heroes a hard time. Then look for The Watcher and yet another piece of the Ultimate Nullifier.

Mickey the Mouth

Hairy Harrison

Pointy Pickens

Piece of the Ultimate Nullifier

No-Neck Jones

Shady McShade

The Watcher

Wally Worrywart

Doctor Doom has unleashed an army of Doombots to wreak havoc. And to top it off, Galactus is lurking! Wade into the battle and help The Avengers and The Fantastic Four find these things, including The Watcher and a piece of the Ultimate Nullifier, the only weapon that will stop Galactus.

H.E.R.B.I.E.

A man practicing his putting

Lockjaw

Piece of the Ultimate Nullifier

This window washer

The Watcher

Our heroes finally have the Ultimate Nullifier, the only thing that will stop Galactus. Find this important weapon, The Watcher, and these brave Avengers who are battling to save the world.

Iron Man

Wasp

Captain America

The Ultimate Nullifier

The Watcher

Ant-Man

Hawkeye

Black Widow

Sneak back into The Red Skull's lair to find more weapons. This time, find these things that The Red Skull might use against our heroes.

Turn back to the city and find these traffic signs on the bustling and chaotic streets.

YIELD

NO PARKING BUS STOP

STOP

SLOW

BROADWAY

Head back to the Academy grounds and find these textbooks used to teach new mutant heroes.

Advanced Calculus

A Tale of Two Cities

Culture & Civilization

Economics

AMERICAN HISTORY

Creep back to the graveyard and find these goofy, ghoulish tombstone markings.

Noah Moore Is no more

Daisy Pushing

Hamlet Good night sweet prince

This bloke went up in smoke

Silly Sally held her breath and now she's breathed her last

Sherry Cherry Choked on a chokecherry

Boogie back to the beach to find this sandy summer stuff.

Cruise back to the wharf and find these things in and around the warehouse.

Soar back to the rooftops of the city skyline and find these defeated Doombots.

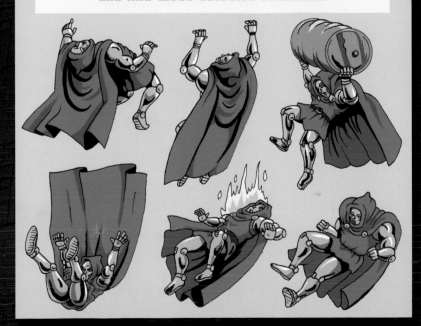

Hurry back to the final battle scene and give The Avengers a hand by spotting these six villainous ne'er-do-wells.

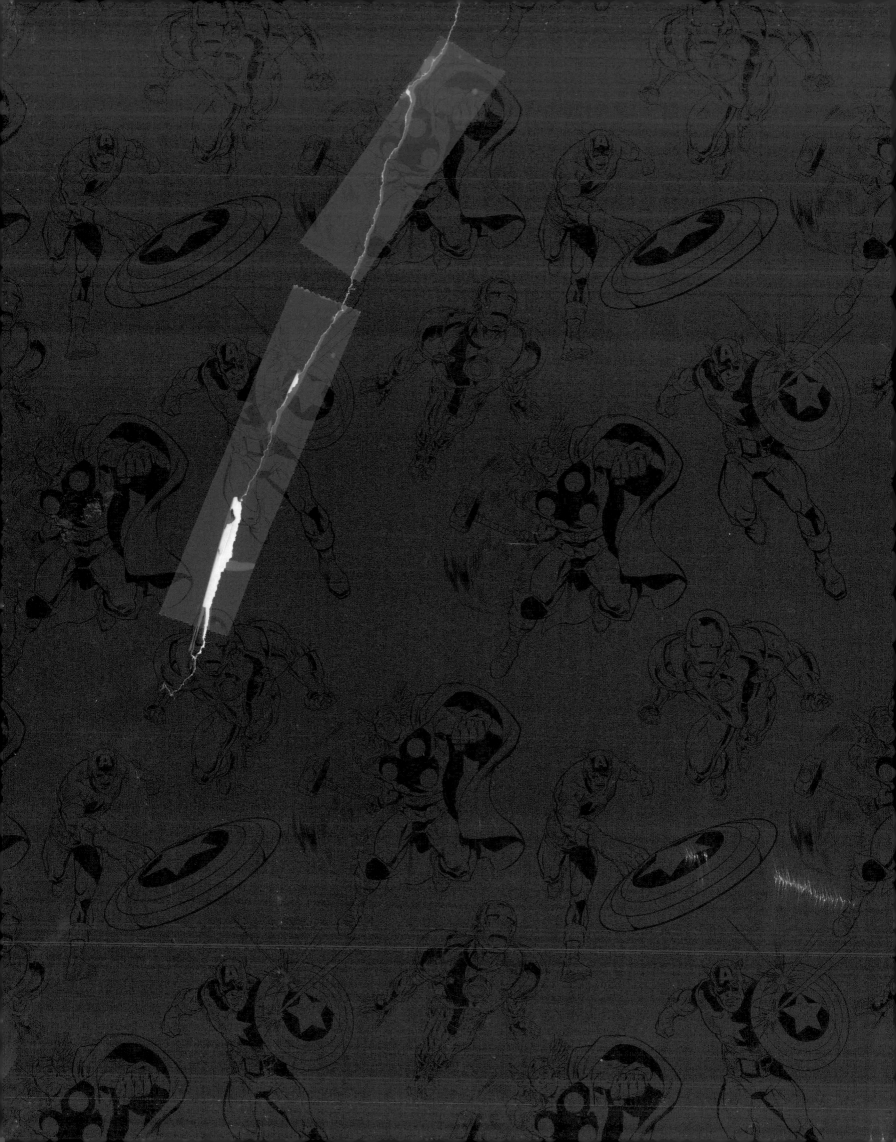